FLY FISHING! #@%&*!

Cartoons by John Troy

NICK LYONS BOOKS

Printed in the United States of America

10 9 8 7 6 5 4

Library of Congress Catalog Card Number: 84-062705

Some of the cartoons in this book have appeared previously in the following magazines:
Field & Stream, Wisconsin Sportsman, Fly Fishing, The In-Fisherman, Trout,
and *Fly Fisherman.*

Waiter, there's a fly in this soup.

How was Opening Day, sweetheart?

When you said an early season float trip I thought, perhaps, in a canoe or a johnboat on a quiet trout stream in North Carolina or Virginia, rather than here on a block of ice in the Kokolik River in northern Alaska.

I'll have a Ginger Quill, and make it extra dry, please.

This is Mr. Edwards. He ties our midges.

I'm afraid that's not quite right, Mr. Purvis.

As nice an "S" cast as I've ever seen, Mr. Finlay, but I was thinking more in terms of a capital "S", and not necessarily in script.

What makes you think fly fishing is difficult to learn?

You certainly had a nice cast going there, young man.

You would never know it, but I haven't used a fly rod in years.

There, there, Mr. Fletcher, the world doesn't begin and end with a fanwing
Royal Coachman.

What's this I hear about you coming up with a revolutionary neck hackle?

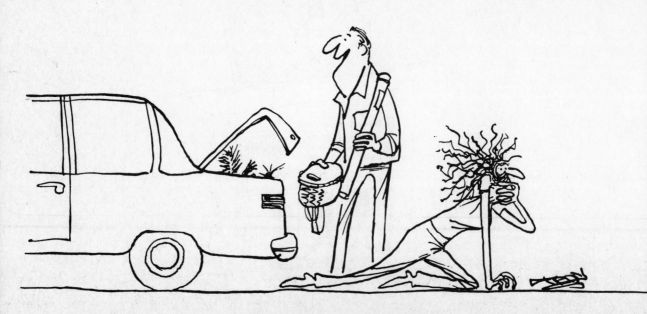

Ah, you've seen my "roadkills."

Aren't you overdoing this roadkill thing a bit?

Feel cooler, honey?

Matching The Hatch

It's one of those "Look casual but beat the other guy to the fishing hole" routines.

Psst.

It was inevitable—a compound fly rod!

Dry flies float, wet flies sink—that's all you have to know for now!

I caught them on a size twelve Dark Hendrickson dry fly. What are you using?

I was wasting away on booze and drugs—man, then I discovered fly fishing.

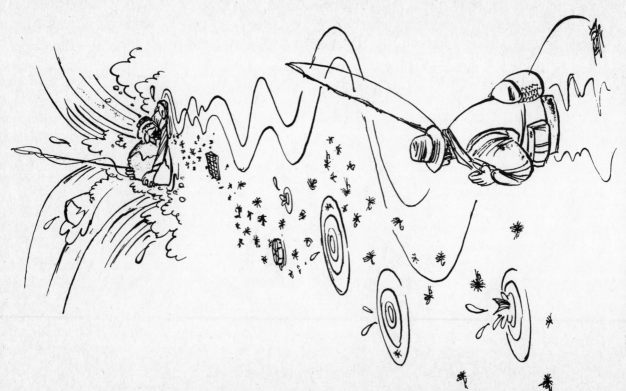

Never mind me, which fly are they rising to?!

Tie your own flies?

I forgot my fly rod.

They'll start to rise at noon. Take my word for it—I know.

He's not so smart. He thinks they're trout, but they're only chubs.

I just never expected to see you on this stretch of the river.

Do you think that, somehow, they *know*?

I've heard of low profile stalking, but this is ridiculous.

Is this what you're sneaking up on?!

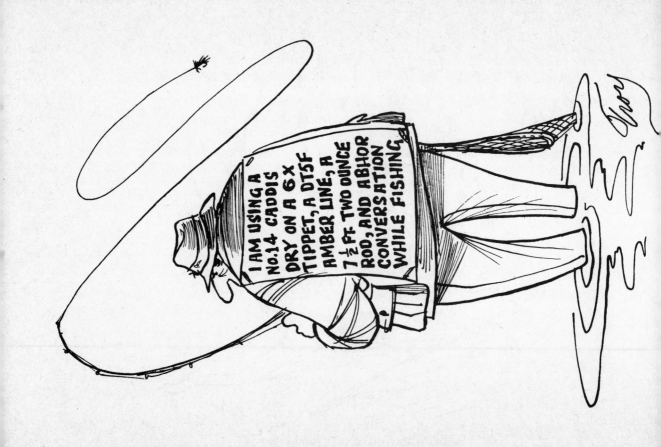

You don't see many rises like this.

Ah, what luck!

I'm sorry, I don't question the fairness of laws, I just enforce them.

Well, well, I've accidentally gotten a worm on the hook my fly fell off of!

Sorry

I'd sure like to find out why my flies keep breaking off.

Darn automatic reels!

So that's what you're catching them on, eh, the size 28 tricos . . . KERCHOO!

They're not only educated, they're downright insulting!

Remember those "bargain-basement" waders I bought last week . . .?

Still determined to catch that lunker trout on a dry fly?

Yes, I would say large brown trout can be described as being predominantely cannibalistic. Why do you ask?

Let me guess—this is your first salmon.

To tell you the truth I'm afraid to set the hook!

Quick, hit the pocket over there with your Muddler!

Best cutthroat guide in the business.

Sure he's small, and I often have to wait for him to catch up, but he's dynamite on those midge hatches.

You may find this hard to believe, but at one time I was a well known fly fisherman.

Wow, you talk *fresh*!

He said he'd land that forty-pound salmon on that 6X tippet if it takes him all day. That was last Tuesday.

What a pleasant surprise, and just what kind of fly fishing do you do?

Edwin lives for salmon fishing.

You'll never know how much George has been looking forward to your party.

I don't think George really cares for the Islands.

So what are you doing after the party?

I didn't know whether to go fishing or have a party, so . . .

Why can't you be like other men and think of nothing but sex, sex, sex!

Will it help our relationship if I throw it back?

May I have a new fly? This one is all mussed up.

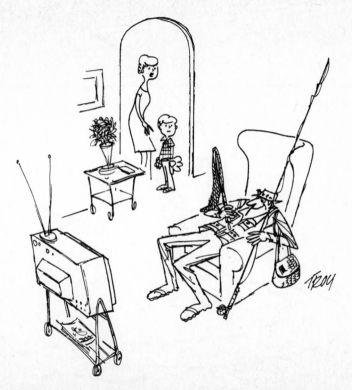

Don't disturb your father—he's fishing for rainbow trout in New Zealand with Curt Gowdy.

A man on *American Sportsman* was fishing with worms.

Your "Hovering Mayfly" is certainly unique, Mr. Benson, and I'm sure we can do business should you ever get its weight below the present seventeen pounds.

It was her late husband's most prized possession and she wouldn't part with it, so I bought the old lady, too.